Walking the Straight Path

DL Publicaciones

Cali, Colombia

Copyright © 2002, 2012 by DL Publicaciones
All rights reserved. Edition 1.1.1.PE published August 2002
Edition 2.1.1.PE May 2012
ISBN 978-958-8626-10-9

This book includes images from Corel Gallery ™ Magic which are protected by the copyright
laws of the U.S., Canada and elsewhere, and used under license.

DL Publicaciones
Cra. 101 #11B-20
Cali, Colombia
Email: books@devlp.org
Web site: www.devlp.org

About This Publication

DL Publicaciones (DLP) is a nongovernmental organization, currently based in Colombia, dedicated to the dissemination of educational materials designed to enhance the moral and scientific capabilities of individuals, communities, and their institutions. At this stage in its evolution, DLP is primarily occupied with the publication and distribution of a series of textbooks for junior youth—young people from 12 to 15 years old, whose potential to grow into active promoters of the well-being of their communities is so great. In developing the series, DLP connects with organizations around the world that work with junior youth, to give rise to materials that are at once engaging and transformative.

Introduction

Walking the Straight Path is one text in a series that is being developed by DL Publicaciones (DLP) for junior youth. It is assumed that the young people who study it, usually between the ages of 12 and 14, will have mastered the mechanics of reading and writing, will be able to read with ease, and will have begun to acquire the mental skills needed to articulate ideas with some degree of clarity. The book is designed to reinforce that foundation.

To read with good comprehension and to express thoughts clearly are capabilities that every young person should strive to develop. Further, if one is to live a productive and fruitful life in a world of increasing complexity, one must be able to translate high ideals and noble words into pure deeds. Specifically, youthful minds must be given the tools needed to recognize the moral issues underlying the choices they make. Textbooks in the area of language lend themselves readily to the development of this important capability.

Stories have traditionally been used as a means of transmitting moral concepts from one generation to the next. This volume brings together twenty stories from several different cultures, each with a universal theme. Many of the stories are well known and have been recounted in numerous ways. In this sense, they belong to the heritage of humankind. Here they are told in a way that, while stimulating discussion on the moral implications of actions, accommodates exercises that help to build language skills.

The book is intended to be studied by youth in a small group, with the assistance of an "animator", a trained facilitator, who accompanies the group as it moves through the series in its entirety, over the course of three years. Study of the texts, which increase in difficulty with each year, generally begins at age 11 or 12 and is completed by age 15. In addition to study, most groups carry out artistic activities and projects in service to their communities. Such matters are generally decided upon by the youth themselves, who, no longer children, are eager to learn to consult together and make collective decisions. Indeed, it is for this reason that those working with groups are referred to as "animators"; they bring the members together and help create an environment that gives productive shape to their natural energy and enthusiasm.

Animators should note that all twenty lessons in *Walking the Straight Path* adhere to the same format. The story in each is complemented by a series of comprehension questions, which are, in turn, followed by an exercise in vocabulary. Each lesson then presents a question for group discussion and ends with a short quotation for memorization. It is important for animators to bear in mind that the lessons should not be overworked. The youth should read the stories and carry out the exercises relatively quickly. If the animator belabors the exercises, trying to accomplish too much, the lessons will become monotonous and boring. They are best studied at a sprightly pace, in an atmosphere that gives rise to joy and thoughtful reflection.

Walking the Straight Path

I

The wise are not fooled by flattery. Everyone, of course, is encouraged by praise. But let us remember that longing for praise weakens our judgment.

A fox once saw a crow fly off with a piece of cheese in his beak. "I must get that cheese," the fox said to himself and so followed the shadow of the bird until he settled on the branch of a tree.

"Good day, my dear friend," said the fox, putting on his best behavior. "You look so beautiful today. Your feathers are glossy and your eyes shine like jewels. Surely, you have an excellent voice as well. Oh! If only I could hear you sing."

These words were like fresh water satisfying the crow's thirst for praise. So he lifted his head with pride and set out to offer a song in honor of his charming friend.

Of course, the moment he opened his beak, the piece of cheese fell. The fox snapped it up before it hit the ground and ran away, while the crow's not so pleasant voice filled the air.

COMPREHENSION

Answer the questions below in complete sentences.

1. What did the fox see? _____

_____

2. What did the crow have in his beak? _____

_____

3. What did the fox do to get the cheese? _____

_____

4. Did the crow really have a pleasant voice? _____

_____

5. Was the fox sincere in his praise of the crow? _____

_____

6. Did this story occur in a city, village, or forest? _____

_____

VOCABULARY

Complete each of the sentences below using one of the following words:

encouraged, longing, charming,
shadow, praise, satisfied, pride,
pleasant, judgment, weakened

1. The teacher thought her students were hardworking and was always full of _____ for them.

2. Armando and his brother spent a _____ day together, working in the fields and talking about their future plans.

3. Hong Mei liked to travel and had a _____ to see new places.

4. She had a beautiful voice, and her teacher _____ her to study music.

5. The farmer showed good _____ in planting his seeds right after the first rainfall.

6. Chandu was not _____ with the mark he received on his examination, so he decided to study harder.

7. Zhong Jiang was in trouble, but because he had too much _____ , he would not let anyone help him.

2

8. At the end of the day, the long _____ of the tree falls over the garden.

9. It was a _____ story, and the children wanted to listen to it again and again.

10. He was greatly _____ by the illness but soon began to work again, knowing that he would become stronger in time.

DISCUSSION

How do we make sure that we are not fooled by flattery?

MEMORIZATION

"Protect yourselves with utmost vigilance, lest you be entrapped in the snare of deception and fraud."

Looking for faults in others is a dangerous habit. We lose sight of our shortcomings if we waste our time thinking we are superior to others. Would not correcting our own faults be a better use of our energy?

A man well known for his wisdom took his son to a beautiful garden to pray and to meditate. Many others had gathered there for the same purpose. The fragrance of the flowers, the soft whispering of the breeze, and the quiet murmur of a stream created a sense of peace. The father and son sat in the shade of a tree. The boy, following his father's example, closed his eyes and filled his mind with spiritual thoughts. But after some time he became tired. He lost his focus and began to look around, first at the flowers and the birds, and then at the people. To his surprise, he saw that more than half of them were asleep. The boy thought about this: "All these people have come here to pray. They all think they are devoted and religious. But they are not praying. They are just pretending." This bothered him. So he kept thinking about it. And then another thought came to him, a most dangerous thought indeed. He turned to his father and asked, "Are we not better than those who are sleeping instead of praying?"

The father remained silent for a while and then replied, "We might have been, had you not asked that question."

COMPREHENSION

Answer the questions below in complete sentences.

1. Why did the man and his son go to the beautiful garden?

   _____

   _____

2. Were they alone? _____

_____

3. What was there about the garden that created a sense of peace?

_____

_____

4. Where did the father and his son sit? _____

_____

5. What did the boy do, following his father's example? _____

_____

_____

6. When did the boy begin to look around? _____

_____

7. What did the boy see? _____

_____

8. What bothered him? _____

_____

_____

9. What dangerous thought came to him? _____

_____

_____

10. What did he ask his father? _____

_____

_____

11. What was the father's answer? _____

_____

_____

VOCABULARY

Complete each of the sentences below using one of the following words:

superior, shortcomings, focus,
fragrance, murmur, sense, energy,
pretended, dangerous, meditate

1. The roads were slippery because of the rain, so the driver kept his _____ straight ahead.

2. He knows well his own _____ and tries his best to overcome them.

3. It was difficult to understand what she said because she always spoke in a low _____ .

4. Playing in the field, the children _____ to be trees that grew tall in the sunshine.

5. He treated everyone poorly because he felt _____ to them.

6. The flowers gave off a pleasing _____ .

7. He was not one to act hastily; he took time to _____ on each situation before acting.

8. My father was helping our neighbor plow his fields all day and did not have any _____ left in him.

9. The children were playing near the road, but when they were told it was _____ they stopped.

10. Seeing the community progress filled the village council with a _____ of joy.

DISCUSSION

What kinds of thoughts might indicate a feeling of superiority in a person?

MEMORIZATION

"Know ye not why We created you all from the same dust? That no one should exalt himself over the other. Ponder at all times in your hearts how ye were created."

III

Our home, the planet Earth, gives us sustenance and holds for us unimaginable wealth. If we spend all of this wealth, what will be left for those who come after us? Taking good care of our home, its waters, its air, its soil, and its millions of plants and animals is a duty that must not be overlooked. Should we not leave for the next generation an Earth even more plentiful than the one we received from our forefathers.

A king went riding through the countryside to observe the condition of his people. Passing by a field, he noticed a very old man. Although weak and obviously in great pain, he was working hard planting date trees.

The king stopped his horse and asked, "Old man, what are you doing? Surely at your age you should be resting at home enjoying the loving attention of your children."

"O Great King," answered the old man. "I cannot rest yet. I must finish planting these trees."

"How long will it be before they produce fruit for your pleasure?" inquired the king.

"These trees will not see fruit for at least twenty years!" was the answer.

"What is your haste then? Surely you will not live to eat the fruits of the trees you are so diligently planting," observed the king.

"You are correct, my Master," replied the old man. "However my forefathers planted trees whose fruits I have enjoyed all my life. It is now my duty to plant for the benefit of the next generation."

The king was so pleased by this answer that he gave the man a gold coin.

"I thank you, Great King," said the man smiling. "Just planting the trees was reward enough for me. But now these trees have already borne fruit. This coin is worth more than what the first harvest would bring."

COMPREHENSION

Answer the questions below in complete sentences.

1. For what purpose was the king riding through the country-side? _____

_____

2. How would you describe the man the king noticed? _____

_____

3. What did the king think the man should be doing? _____

_____

_____

4. When did the man think he could rest? _____

_____

_____

5. How long would it take for the date trees to produce fruit?

_____

_____

6. Would the man be able to enjoy the fruits of the trees he was planting? _____

_____

7. For whom was the man planting the trees? _____

   _____

8. What reward did the man expect? _____

   _____

9. Why did the man say the trees had already borne fruit? _____

   _____

   _____

   _____

VOCABULARY

Complete each of the sentences below using one of the following
words:

> sustenance, unimaginable, wealth,
> plentiful, reward, haste, diligently,
> generation, observing, overlooked

1. The little girl ran home to her mother; she was in great
   _____ .

2. The harvest was _____ this season, and our
   village has enough food for the next year.

3. She enjoyed walking in the forest, _____ the
   many plants and animals.

4. He worked _____ and finished repairing the
   table on time.

5. May the youth of today be the _____ that
   brings peace to the world.

6. It is _____ that a noble person would ever
   tell a lie.

7. He knew that his family's _____ depended on hard work and God's blessings.

8. Every stone, every drop of water, every tree, every animal is part of the _____ the Earth holds for humanity.

9. There is no greater _____ for a teacher than watching his students progress.

10. Katherine did her homework with such haste that she _____ two of the exercises.

DISCUSSION

What can you and your friends do to care for the planet Earth?

MEMORIZATION

"Say: Nature in its essence is the embodiment of My Name, the Maker, the Creator."

IV

There are times when we all need something that we do not have. To work for that which we desire is worthy of praise. However, if it is not controlled, desire can become greed, and greed can become our master.

A dog found a nice juicy bone lying in the trash. He quickly grabbed it and headed home, imagining all the time the pleasure of eating the bone in peace. On the way, he had to cross a small river that ran through the village. As he stepped on the plank used for crossing, his eyes fell on a delightful sight. There in the calm waters of the river was another dog, just like himself, with a delicious looking bone in his mouth.

"This is really my lucky day," he thought. "Surely I can take away that bone from this silly dog. By the time he gets out of the water, I will have reached home." But the moment he opened his mouth, his own bone fell into the water and disappeared. All he could see, then, was the other dog staring back at him with a sad look on his face. It was the face of a disappointed dog who had lost not one but two delicious meals.

COMPREHENSION

Answer the questions below in complete sentences.

1. What did the dog find lying in the trash? _____

   _____

2. What was the dog imagining while he headed home with the

   bone? _____

   _____

13

3. What delightful sight did the dog see while crossing the river?

_____

_____

_____

4. What do you think he really saw? _____

_____

5. What do you think kept the dog from seeing what was really

there? _____

_____

6. Why did he think he would be able to take the second bone and

get away? _____

_____

_____

7. What happened when he tried to take the other bone? _____

_____

_____

8. How did the dog feel after losing both bones? _____

_____

VOCABULARY

Complete each of the sentences on the next page using one of the
following words:

> delightful, delicious, pleasure,
> plank, greed, desire, disappeared,
> controlled, disappointed, worthy

1. It is always a _____ to meet people with a smile on their face.

2. She was _____ in herself when she realized that she could have studied harder and done better on the exam.

3. The mango was so _____ that he bought five more.

4. One bench was made with a flat _____ , while the others were made with round logs.

5. The four friends spent the afternoon together and had a _____ time.

6. Because of her strong _____ to help people, she decided to become a doctor.

7. Because of his _____ , he kept raising the prices in his store until, one by one, he lost his customers.

8. The moon _____ behind the cloud.

9. Although he was very upset, he _____ his anger.

10. He was very humble and did not think he was _____ of all the praise he received for being first in his class.

DISCUSSION

Is it a sign of greed to want to improve our lives?

MEMORIZATION

"Concern yourselves with the things that benefit mankind, and not with your corrupt and selfish desires."

V

Sometimes we are faced with a task that seems impossible. But if we persevere, we may be surprised at what we can achieve. Perseverance is one of the keys to success. The story of the Rabbit and the Turtle is a good example.

All of Rabbit's friends knew that he was the fastest among them. More than anyone else, Rabbit knew it, and he never tired of telling his friends. Oh, how they wished Rabbit would stop bragging about his running skills. But no one knew what to do about it. Then something unexpected happened. To everyone's surprise, Turtle challenged Rabbit to a long-distance race.

At the appointed hour, all the animals gathered to watch. The signal was given and the race began. There was a loud whooooosh, and Rabbit was out of sight.

Turtle put his head down and took the first step, then another . . . and another . . . and another. The animals went to the finish line and waited. Meanwhile, Rabbit was having a merry time. He ran and hopped and skipped. He felt like singing. "Why should I strain myself?" he thought. "How can Turtle possibly win?" Feeling slightly fatigued after all his hopping and skipping, he stopped behind a tree and lay down to rest. Soon he was in a deep sleep.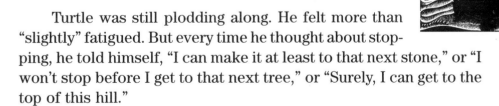

Turtle was still plodding along. He felt more than "slightly" fatigued. But every time he thought about stopping, he told himself, "I can make it at least to that next stone," or "I won't stop before I get to that next tree," or "Surely, I can get to the top of this hill."

And so Turtle plodded along. Time passed. Rabbit dreamed happily away. The animals waited. Finally they saw Turtle come into sight. And while Rabbit was dreaming of success, Turtle, breathing heavily and exhausted, crossed the finish line.

COMPREHENSION

Answer the questions below in complete sentences.

1. What did all of Rabbit's friends know? _____

   _____

2. What did Rabbit think of his own ability to run? _____

   _____

   _____

3. Why do you think Turtle challenged Rabbit to a long-distance

   race? _____

   _____

   _____

4. How did Rabbit begin the race? _____

   _____

5. How did Turtle begin the race? _____

   _____

6. Why did Rabbit stop to sleep? _____

   _____

   _____

7. How did Turtle feel after a while? _____

   _____

8. How did Turtle keep himself going? _____

   _____

9. What was Rabbit doing when Turtle crossed the finish line?

_____

_____

VOCABULARY

Complete each of the sentences below using one of the following words:

slightly, challenged, persevered,
unexpectedly, gathered, fatigued,
brag, straining, plodded, surprised

1. Our neighboring village _____ us to a football game.

2. Tired from a long day's work, they _____ along the road towards home.

3. After playing soccer, all of the boys were more than a little _____ .

4. My older brother and his family who live in the city returned to our village _____ .

5. The mechanic gave up too easily; he could have fixed the truck if he had just _____ .

6. He realized that it was not correct for him to _____ about his new bicycle to his friends.

7. The climber was _____ to reach the top of the mountain before nightfall.

8. One of the twins is _____ taller than the other.

9. The children _____ around their grand-father to listen to his stories.

10. She was _____ when she looked at her watch and found that an hour had passed.

DISCUSSION

How much can we achieve in our lives without perseverance?

MEMORIZATION

"The main thing is to remain staunch and firmly rooted, and persevere to the end."

VI

Not much can be gained without effort. Those who give in to discouragement have defeated themselves. Victory comes to the one who tries and tries again. Take the example of these two frogs.

 With a scream,

two frogs fell into a deep bowl of cream.

The first was a persistent kind of soul,

but the other took the gloomy role.

"We'll drown," he lamented, and with a despairing cry

he flung up his legs and said, "Goodbye!"

Said the first frog with a determined grin,

"I can't get out, but I won't give in.

I'll swim around till my strength is spent,

then, if I must, I'll die content."

Bravely he swam to work his scheme,

and his struggles began to churn the cream.

The more he swam, his legs aflutter,

the more the cream turned into butter.

On top of the butter at last he stopped,

and out of the bowl he gaily hopped.

COMPREHENSION

Answer the questions below in complete sentences.

1. What did the frogs fall into? _____

    _____

2. How would you describe the character of the first frog?

    _____

3. How would you describe the character of the second frog?

    _____

4. What happened to the second frog? _____

    _____

5. What decision did the first frog make? _____

    _____

    _____

6. What does cream turn into when it is beaten? _____

    _____

7. What did the struggles of the first frog bring? _____

    _____

8. What happened next? _____

    _____

VOCABULARY

Complete each of the sentences below using one of the following words:

> gained, gloomy, despair, flung,
> lamented, persistent, defeated,
> scheme, churning, determined

1. Eager to start the day, she _____ back the covers
    and jumped out of bed.

2. When he walked in the room and saw their _____
    faces, he knew that something was wrong.

3. It is easy to see her _____ nature by watching her try and try again when she is faced with a problem.

4. So polluted had the river become that the villagers were in _____ , thinking they would never enjoy it again.

5. A new _____ to clean up the river was placed before the village council.

6. After the river had been cleaned, the whole community was _____ not to allow it to fall into the same condition again.

7. He _____ his decision not to join the group when he saw how happily all the members worked together.

8. The children enjoyed walking through the shallow water _____ up the mud.

9. Although she had not reached her goal, she did not let herself feel _____ and kept on going.

10. All the students who participated in the community service project _____ extra credits in school.

DISCUSSION

Which do you appreciate more: something you gained after much effort or something that came to you easily?

MEMORIZATION

> **"Absolute repose does not exist in nature. All things either make progress or lose ground."**

VII

We continually receive the bounties of God. But life does not offer us only sweetness. We must have our share of pain and sorrow if we are to grow and draw close to Him. Remembering with gratitude our moments of joy helps us to avoid bitterness in times of difficulty.

There once was a just and powerful king who had won the loyalty of all his people, high and low. His court was filled with the most accomplished individuals in the kingdom. Yet his favorite was a servant who had attended him selflessly for many years. The other members of the court were envious of this humble man and took every opportunity to convince the king that he was not sincere in his devotion. But the king knew his servant too well to ever doubt him.

One day when the king was enjoying a great feast, he called his loyal servant to his presence and offered him a delicious looking piece of melon. The servant ate it with enjoyment. The king offered him another and another until nearly the whole melon had disappeared. Seeing the pleasure with which the servant ate the melon, the king decided to taste it. His eyes widened in surprise when he found it bitter and disagreeable. "Why, this is very bitter! How could you eat it with such joy?" he asked.

"You have brought so much sweetness to your kingdom with your justice and compassion," replied the servant, "that I thought one bitter melon was not worth mentioning."

Once again it was proved that the servant's sincerity could not be questioned.

COMPREHENSION

Answer the questions below in complete sentences.

1. What were some of the qualities of the king in this story? _____

_____

2. What kind of people filled the king's court? _____

   _loyal Servants_____

3. Whom did the king favor most? _Servants_____

   _____

4. Why do you think the king favored this servant? _____

   _they were loyal_____

   _____

5. How did the other members of the court feel about the servant?

   _invious_____

   _____

6. Of what did they try to convince the king? _____

   _____

7. What did the king offer to his servant during the feast? _____

   _melons_____

   _____

8. What did the king discover when he tasted the melon? _____

   _liked the king_____

   _____

9. Why could the servant eat the bitter melon with such joy? _____

   _____

   _____

VOCABULARY

Complete each of the sentences below using one of the following words:

> selflessly, loyalty, accomplished,
> sorrow, presence, avoid, gratitude,
> disagreeable, convinced, sincere

1. Often, during prayer, we feel to be in the _presence_ of God.

2. With no desire for a reward, she _selflessly_ assisted her neighbor.

3. We all feel _sorrow_ when we see the suffering of people around us.

4. She studied, learned, and became a very _accomplished_ person.

5. Because of her love for her children, she carried out with joy even the most _disagreeable_ tasks.

6. Friendship requires _loyalty_ .

7. Ivan could only remember with _gratitude_ the sacrifices his parents made to educate him.

8. If you are in a hurry, you should _avoid_ going through the marketplace.

9. He is a _sincere_ friend, one with whom I can share my thoughts.

10. I did not want to attend the meeting, but I am glad that he _convinced_ me to go.

DISCUSSION

What is the difference between sorrow and bitterness?

MEMORIZATION

"To express his gratitude for the favors of God man must show forth praiseworthy actions."

VIII

"No man is an island" is a phrase frequently quoted the world over. Alone, none of us can get very far. Community life is an essential part of our existence.

 In a community that enjoyed much warmth and unity, one individual became discouraged and kept away from the others. The local council asked a friend to help him overcome his feelings of estrangement. Soon the friend invited him to his house for dinner and, in a most natural way, showered him with kindness. It was a chilly night, and following dinner the two sat in front of the fire sipping tea and watching the flames.

After a few minutes, the host had an idea. He picked up a brightly burning piece of wood with a pair of tongs and moved it to a corner of the fireplace. He sat back in silence while his guest kept watching. Alone, the ember began to lose its fire until there was a last glow and then coldness and death. Before the evening was over, he moved the cold dead wood to the middle of the fire where it became a glowing ember once again.

Not a word was said all evening about the whole matter. But when the guest was almost out the door, he turned around and said, "Thank you for the fiery lesson." At the next community gathering, everyone was happy to see a friend who had been sorely missed.

COMPREHENSION

Answer the questions below in complete sentences.

1. In what kind of community did the story take place? _____

    _____

    _____

2. What caused one individual to keep away from the others?

_____

_____

3. Why did the friend invite this man to his home for dinner?

_____

_____

_____

4. What did the two men do after dinner? _____

_____

_____

5. What happened to the piece of wood when it was removed from

the fire? _____

_____

6. What matter was not discussed all evening? _____

_____

7. What did the guest mean by the "fiery lesson"? _____

_____

_____

8. What effect did the evening have on the discouraged man?

_____

_____

_____

Complete each of the sentences below using one of the following words:

> matter, discouraged, overcome,
> frequently, estrangement, fiery,
> glow, quote, individual, essential

1. Most difficulties can be _____ with hard work.

2. Toshiko felt very strongly about the need to care for the environment and gave a _____ speech on the dangers of pollution.

3. In the darkness of the night, the group of friends enjoyed the _____ of the lamp.

4. A large supply of fresh, clean water is _____ for the health of the community.

5. In spite of ill health, Martha was not _____ .

6. He was upset about something but would not say what; he said that it was a private _____ and did not want to discuss it.

7. She did not want their misunderstanding to be the cause of their _____ , so she made a special effort to listen to him.

8. My brother is curious about everything and _____ asks questions.

9. He has an excellent memory and was able to _____ the passage word for word.

10. Every _____ who wants to attend the meeting is welcome.

DISCUSSION

What should friends do when they feel that, for some reason, they are becoming estranged from one another?

MEMORIZATION

"Shut your eyes to estrangement, then fix your gaze
   upon unity."

IX

As we rise to excellence, we find many spiritual forces at our command. One of these forces is kindness. A simple act of kindness can overcome even the most ferocious of beasts, as a slave in ancient Roman times once discovered.

Androcles was a slave who had managed to escape from his cruel master. Moving quietly through the forest, he suddenly came upon a lion. Fear seized him, and he began to run from the ferocious beast. After only a few steps though, he noticed that the lion was not following. So he stopped and went back to see what was happening. The lion was lying on the ground with a swollen and bloodied paw, and Androcles could see a large thorn in it. The suffering of so noble a beast touched his heart. He overcame his fear, approached the lion, and gently pulled out the thorn. He then went on to bind the wound with a strip of fabric torn from his own clothes. In this way, Androcles and the lion became friends.

Unfortunately, Androcles was later captured by the emperor's soldiers. As an escaped slave, he was sentenced to fight a hungry lion in front of the emperor and a large crowd. This usually meant death.

On the day of the fight, Androcles was placed in the arena. He prepared himself to meet his fate. A lion was released from a cage. Growling fiercely, it leaped towards its victim. Then suddenly it stopped. It approached Androcles slowly, licked his hand, and received a hug in return. The two friends had met once again.

The crowd called for Androcles to be freed. The emperor summoned him to his presence. When he heard the story of this unusual friendship, he gave Androcles his freedom and released the lion to roam the forests.

COMPREHENSION

Answer the questions below in complete sentences.

1. Who was Androcles? _____

_____

2. From whom was he escaping? _____

_____

3. What did he suddenly find in the forest? _____

_____

4. What did he do first? _____

_____

5. What did he see when he stopped and looked more carefully?

_____

_____

6. How did Androcles and the lion become friends? _____

_____

_____

_____

7. To what was Androcles sentenced when he was captured?

_____

_____

8. What was the expected result of this sentence? _____

_____

9. When it was released into the arena, how did the lion behave at first? _____

_____

10. What happened next? _____

_____

_____

11. What did the emperor do when he heard the story of the friend-ship between Androcles and the lion? _____

_____

_____

_____

VOCABULARY

Complete each of the sentences below using one of the following words:

> captured, prepared, suffering,
> released, sentence, approached,
> summon, roam, ancient, swollen

1. Yesterday he sprained his ankle and now it is _____ and painful.

2. It was interesting to see all of the _____ tools in the museum.

3. The judge may _____ anyone to the court for questioning.

4. The judge is very fair, and he always makes sure that his _____ fits the crime.

5. She _____ herself for work every day by thinking about the things she would do, one by one.

6. In the spring, after the cold weather has passed, the cattle are _____ into the fields and allowed to roam freely.

7. During the summer months, the cattle _____ the countryside freely.

8. The train slowed down as it _____ the station.

9. He _____ her heart through his kindness and gentleness.

10. Anger and hatred can only lead to _____ .

DISCUSSION

Are there times when we should not show kindness to others?

MEMORIZATION

"Do not be content with showing friendship in words alone, let your heart burn with loving kindness for all who may cross your path."

X

It is not always easy to make choices about the direction of our lives. One voice may tell us to rise to excellence and another, equally strong, may try to keep us down. Here is the story of an eagle that listened to the right voice.

A nest high on a magnificent mountain contained a few large eagle eggs. One day a strong wind shook the nest, and an egg rolled down the mountainside, coming to rest on a farm. The resident chickens felt they should care for such a gift from heaven, so they asked an old hen to sit on it for a while. She agreed.

This was not the most comfortable thing the hen had ever done, but her care and the heat from her body worked; the egg finally hatched and an eagle was born. Unfortunately for the eagle, he was raised to be a chicken—a rather unusual one, but a chicken nonetheless. And the saddest part of all was that he believed he was nothing more than a chicken. Yet, his spirit longed for something else. Every now and again, especially on bright sunny mornings, he would look up and see eagles in the sky. How he wished that he could fly like those birds. But whenever he mentioned this to the chickens, they would make fun of him and cackle, "A chicken who wants to fly!"

Then one day, an eagle, probably his own brother or sister, flew low over the farm and called out to him, "Why are you down there and not up here flying with us?"

"I'm a chicken," he answered. "I can't fly."

"Of course you can fly," the eagle responded. "You're an eagle like me. Look at your wings. Are those the wings of a chicken?"

"But I can't fly," was his unhappy reply.

"Yes you can. Do as I am."

And so, with some hesitation, our eagle spread his mighty wings for the first time. To his surprise, he soon found himself soaring in the skies.

COMPREHENSION

Answer the questions below in complete sentences.

1. Where were the eagle eggs? _____

   _____

2. What happened to one of the eggs when a strong wind shook

   the nest? _____

   _____

   _____

3. How did the chickens react to the arrival of the egg? _____

   _____

   _____

4. What was born from the egg? _____

   _____

5. How was the eagle raised? _____

   _____

6. What did the eagle believe? _____

   _____

7. For what did his spirit long? _____

   _____

8. When the eagle mentioned his longing, how did the chickens

respond? _____

_____

9. Why did the eagle think that he could not fly? _____

_____

10. To whom did the eagle listen in the end? _____

_____

VOCABULARY

Complete each of the sentences below using one of the following words:

> choice, resident, comfortable,
> raised, shook, soared, agreed,
> contains, unusual, hesitation

1. When the breeze came, the kites _____ in the sky.

2. Parvis moved to the town several years ago. He is now considered a long-term _____ of the town.

3. John's parents _____ him to always tell the truth.

4. He could not swim, so he walked into the river with some _____ .

5. He _____ with cold when he came out of the water.

6. The young man offered her the chair that looked the most _____ .

7. All the farmers in the area bring their harvest to the market, so there is a wide _____ of fruits and vegetables.

8. She _____ to stay after school every afternoon to help the younger students in mathematics.

9. It is _____ for it to be so cold at this time of the year.

10. The cookbook _____ one hundred recipes.

DISCUSSION

What are some of the goals we should set for ourselves?

MEMORIZATION

"Noble have I created thee, yet thou hast abased thyself. Rise then unto that for which thou wast created."

XI

One of the greatest joys in life is serving others. But, when we offer our assistance, we should do so unselfishly, without hope of reward or favor.

Mashenka and Dashenka were twin sisters who always managed to figure things out together. One day, they went into the woods to pick berries. After a while, they came upon an old woman struggling to carry a bucket of water from the river to her cabin nearby. Mashenka and Dashenka immediately went to help. The woman was grateful for their assistance and handed them each a freshly baked muffin as thanks. On the way home, the girls eagerly ate up the treat they had received.

When the sisters went into the woods to collect herbs the following day, they saw the old woman hanging her washing out to dry and again offered to help. The woman gladly accepted. She sang a happy tune, while the girls finished the task, and thanked them as they continued on their way in search of herbs, Mashenka whistling the tune she had learned.

The next day the two girls headed off into the woods, this time to gather sticks for the fire. Soon they spotted the old woman. She, too, was gathering sticks. Mashenka said to her sister, "Let us go and help her."

"Why should we?" Dashenka asked. "She did not give us anything last time."

"True, Dashenka," her sister responded. "But the muffins she gave us the other day are no more, and the song she taught us yesterday is still in our hearts." So she went to assist the woman, and Dashenka followed reluctantly behind.

As the sisters walked back to the cabin, each with a bundle of sticks, Mashenka said to the old woman, "Please teach us another song." But the woman only smiled and thanked them for their trouble.

Now Mashenka was more disappointed than Dashenka. "You were right," Mashenka lamented as they made their way home. "The old woman was not truly grateful for our help."

Dashenka was thoughtful for a few moments and responded, "The old woman did teach us something after all. Maybe, when we help someone, we should not expect anything in return, not even gratitude." The two girls looked at each other. Suddenly it was they who were grateful. And when they finally reached home, there was a basket of muffins waiting for them on the doorstep.

COMPREHENSION

Answer the questions below in complete sentences.

1. How many times did Mashenka and Dashenka go into the woods in the story? _____

   _____

2. Who did the sisters see each time they went into the woods?

   _____

3. What was the old woman doing the first time the sisters saw her? _____

   _____

4. What was the old woman doing the second time the sisters saw her? _____

   _____

5. What was the old woman doing the third time the sisters saw her? _____

   _____

6. Why did the old woman give the sisters muffins the first time

   they met? _____

   _____

7. How did the sisters learn the song from the old woman the

   second time they met? _____

   _____

8. Why was Dashenka reluctant to help the old woman the third

   time they met? _____

   _____

   _____

9. What did Mashenka hope that she and her sister would learn

   from the old woman the third time they met? _____

   _____

10. Why were the girls grateful to the old woman in the end? ___

    _____

11. Where did the basket of muffins come from? _____

    _____

Vocabulary

Complete each of the sentences on the next page using one of the
following words:

> struggling, assistance, grateful,
> reluctant, accepted, spotted,
> expect, fresh, manage, bundle

1. Janis was _____ that the bus arrived just as it started to rain.

2. The young girl needed _____ in tying her shoes because she was still learning to do it by herself.

3. The dog _____ the cat in the tree and started to bark.

4. He graciously _____ the plate of food that was offered to him.

5. After a long day at work, his father was _____ to stay awake while watching the movie.

6. With the invention of refrigeration, it is possible for food to stay _____ for a longer time.

7. Though Gus ran as fast as he could for the bus, he did not _____ to catch it and had to walk to town instead.

8. She was _____ to ask her brother Ray for help because she knew that he was so busy with work.

9. The merchant was a trustworthy man, and the farmer knew that she could always _____ to receive a fair price for the grain she grew.

10. At the market the fisherman uses a piece of newspaper to wrap freshly caught fish into a _____.

DISCUSSION

How should we feel when our good deeds are not acknowledged?

MEMORIZATION

"... unto them that are rid of all attachments a deed is, verily, its own reward."

XII

Perseverance is an admirable quality. We often need to set goals for ourselves and strive to meet them. But there is a difference between perseverance and obsession.

The hunter picked up his gear and went in search of prey. While he was laying his traps, a beautiful bird caught his eye. So enchanting was the bird that he began to follow it. After a while, he forgot that he was hunting for food and concentrated on the bird, which he thought could be sold for a good price in the market.

But the bird was not easy to catch. It seemed to read the hunter's mind. Just as he was about to capture it, it would fly to the next tree and sit on a branch waiting, as if it were teasing him. Gradually, catching the bird became the hunter's obsession. He would run, he would pause, and he would sneak up on the bird. It was exhausting. Once he failed to notice a rock in his way and fell.

Then he became angry, which made him careless. His reckless movements attracted the attention of a hungry wolf. But he was so intent on catching the beautiful bird that he did not notice the wolf behind him. When he finally did, the wolf was about to leap on him.

He ran to a tree and climbed it as fast as he could. As he sat on a branch looking in fear at the wolf below, he realized that because of his obsession he was not the hunter anymore; the hunter had become the prey.

COMPREHENSION

Answer the questions below in complete sentences.

1. What caught the hunter's eye? _____

_____

2. What was the hunter doing when he saw the bird? _____

_____

3. What did the hunter forget while concentrating on the bird?

_____

_____

4. What did the bird do to tease the hunter? _____

_____

_____

5. What did the hunter do that shows he was obsessed with the

bird? _____

_____

6. What attracted the wolf's attention? _____

_____

7. What did the hunter do to escape the wolf? _____

_____

8. What had the hunter become because of his obsession? _____

_____

_____

VOCABULARY

Complete each of the sentences on the next page using one of the
following words:

> enchanting, attracted, admirable,
> careless, exhausting, concentrate,
> intent, reckless, obsession, notice

46

1. She found the music _____ and sat listening to it for hours.

2. Removing the large rocks from the field was _____ work, but it had to be done before the field could be planted.

3. Fashion had become an _____ for her, and she could think and talk of nothing else.

4. No one would hire Joao, for it was well known that he was _____ in his work.

5. Vivian was so _____ on finishing her work that she forgot to call her friend.

6. Carmen Elisa decided to leave other tasks for later and to _____ on her homework.

7. He had his license taken away because of his _____ driving.

8. The moths were _____ to the light and circled around it in great numbers.

9. She did not _____ that the window was open, and when it started to rain, the rug became soaking wet.

10. Courage is an _____ quality; but if it does not go hand in hand with wisdom, it can turn into recklessness.

DISCUSSION

How can we tell the difference between perseverance and obsession?

MEMORIZATION

"In all matters moderation is desirable. If a thing is carried to excess, it will prove a source of evil."

XIII

We all have our share of difficulties, but we should not be defeated by them. And when fortune visits us, it is best not to become attached to it. Throughout our lives, joy and sorrow come and go, one after the other.

 A king sent for his minister one day and said to him, "There is a special ring I would like to wear at the great festival in six months' time. I want you to find it and bring it to me."

"I shall do my best, Your Majesty," replied the minister. "Would you tell me what is so special about the ring?"

"It has magic powers," answered the king. "If you are happy and look at it, you become sad, and if you are sad and look at it, you become happy."

The minister set out in search of the ring. Days passed, then weeks and months, and still he had not found it. He was about to give up when, on the morning of the festival, he came across a humble merchant selling a few trinkets spread out on an old mat in the street.

"Have you by any chance heard of a magic ring that makes the happy sad and the sad happy?"

To the minister's surprise, the merchant pulled out a simple ring with a few words engraved on it. "Is this what you are looking for?" he asked eagerly.

The minister strained his eyes, read the words, and immediately realized that he had found the object of his search. He paid the merchant a handsome sum for the ring and returned to the palace in high spirits. The festival was about to begin.

The king was in a joyous mood. When he examined the ring and read the words he became sad. Then he thought for a while, read the words again, and his sadness vanished. He laughed loudly and praised the minister for a job well done.

And what do you think were the words that had such magic? They were simple enough. On the ring was engraved, "This, too, shall pass."

COMPREHENSION

Answer the questions below in complete sentences.

1. What task did the king give to his minister? _____

   _____

   _____

2. How did the minister answer the king? _____

   _____

   _____

3. What was special about the ring the king wanted? _____

   _____

   _____

4. Who did the minister come across on the morning of the festival? _____

   _____

5. What did the merchant show him? _____

   _____

6. How did the king react to the words engraved on the ring?

   _____

   _____

   _____

7. What were the words engraved on the ring? _____

_____

VOCABULARY

Complete each of the sentences below using one of the following words:

merchant, fortune, handsome,
vanished, attached, examining,
mood, strain, eagerly, engraved

1. The old man was thankful for his good _____;
   a healthy grandchild was born to his son and daughter-in-law.

2. There was so much noise in the marketplace that I had to
   _____ my ears to hear the shopkeeper.

3. Sharon enjoyed buying, selling, and bargaining, so she decided
   to become a _____ .

4. It was a _____ horse, and the owner
   thought he could get a good price for it.

5. The news of his safe return home put everyone in a cheerful
   _____ .

6. After _____ Erna's sore shoulder, the
   doctor determined that she had only strained a muscle.

7. The elderly couple were _____ to their home
   and found it difficult to sell it, having lived there for so many
   years.

8. The children missed their father while he was away and
   _____ awaited his return.

9. She said the poem over and over again until the words were
   _____ on her mind.

10. The sun _____ behind the dark clouds and
    it soon began to rain.

DISCUSSION

How would remembering the words engraved on the ring in the story make a difference in your life?

MEMORIZATION

> **"Should prosperity befall thee, rejoice not, and should abasement come upon thee, grieve not, for both shall pass away and be no more."**

XIV

So often we do things without thinking, for habits rule much of our behavior. Would we not profit from examining our thoughts, words, and deeds every once in a while to make sure that we are not behaving like machines?

 It is said that when the famous library of Alexandria burned, all the books were lost but one. Apparently of no value, the book fell into the hands of a poor man, who could read it only with difficulty. He did not find the book very interesting, except for a piece of parchment stuck between two pages. On the parchment was drawn a map on which was marked a spot near the sea. Under the map was written the secret of the "Touchstone!" It explained that the Touchstone, which supposedly could turn copper into gold, was a small pebble hidden somewhere on the seashore among thousands of other pebbles. And what was the secret to finding it? Unlike the ordinary pebbles that were all cold, this special one felt warm to the touch.

The man was delighted. He left his home with a supply of food and traveled to the seashore, where he began his search. He decided to pick the pebbles up one by one and, if they were cold, throw them into the sea. In this way, he was sure to come to the Touchstone sooner or later. So that is what he did for hours, then days, then weeks.

Months had passed, when one morning he started his daily routine as usual: the first pebble was cold and he threw it into the sea. The next one was cold and he threw it into the sea, as was the next, and the next, and the next. Then he picked up a pebble and it was warm. He threw it into the sea. By the time he realized what he had done, it was too late. Following mindlessly the habit he had formed, he missed his chance to possess countless wealth.

COMPREHENSION

Answer the questions below in complete sentences.

1. Where did the book in the story come from? _____

   _____

2. Into whose hands did it fall? _____

   _____

3. What did the man find interesting about the book? _____

   _____

   _____

4. What was on the parchment? _____

   _____

5. What power was the Touchstone believed to have? _____

   _____

   _____

6. How could the Touchstone be found? _____

   _____

   _____

7. How did the man search for the Touchstone? _____

   _____

   _____

   _____

8. Why did the man throw the Touchstone into the sea? _____

_____

_____

_____

VOCABULARY

Complete each of the sentences below using one of the following words:

> behavior, deeds, rules, habit,
> countless, ordinary, possess,
> profited, mindlessly, supply

1. He was walking _____ through the streets, looking in the store windows.

2. While outdoors the children ran around noisily, but once inside they were on their best _____ .

3. Although he never expected a reward, the village council gave him a plaque for all his good _____ .

4. Tania _____ greatly from the extra time she spent improving her reading skills.

5. He has a _____ of whistling when he is fixing something.

6. He wasted _____ hours worrying about what he would wear to the feast.

7. Horses and oxen _____ great strength and are often used to carry heavy loads.

8. My grandmother keeps a _____ of buttons in an old cookie tin.

9. The queen loves her people and _____ them with wisdom and justice.

10. My mother only uses the good tablecloth when we have guests; for the family, she says the _____ one is fine.

DISCUSSION

Why is it important to develop good habits in life?

MEMORIZATION

> **"Be ye on your guard and ever wakeful! Quick-witted and keen of intellect are the faithful, and firm and steadfast are the assured."**

XV

Every day we make dozens of choices: what to do, what not to do, what to say, what not to say. Truthfulness and honesty are the standards by which decisions are to be made. Sometimes it may seem easier to bend the truth a little, but honesty keeps us on the straight path.

 In a far away land the queen was getting old and she had no children. Worried about the future of her kingdom, she was looking for a way to choose an heir.

Late one night, she took a bag of flower seeds and toasted them so that they would never germinate. She then sent a messenger to every town and village inviting youth nearing the age of fifteen to come to the palace. The next day dozens of youth appeared before the queen, eager to find out what she had to say. How delighted they were to hear that one of them would be the future king or queen— the one who could grow the most beautiful flowers from the seeds that had been specially prepared. They each received a handful of seeds and hurried home to plant them. But the seeds, of course, did not germinate.

"People will laugh at me if I have no flowers to present," was the thought on every youth's mind. "I'll be humiliated and the queen will be disappointed."

On the appointed day, the youth returned to the palace. One after the other, they presented the queen with a pot full of flowers, while she shook her head in sadness. Were they all so easily tempted? Was there not one among them with the integrity and courage to follow in her footsteps as the future ruler?

At the end of the line, one youth was holding back his tears. "I am very sorry to disappoint you, Your Majesty," he said. "My seeds did not grow." A smile brightened the queen's face. Jumping up, she threw her arms around the boy. "This is the one! This is the one!" she cried. "My people will be safe with you as their king!"

COMPREHENSION

Answer the questions below in complete sentences.

1. What was the queen worried about? _____

   _____

2. What did the queen do with the flower seeds? _____

   _____

3. What did the youth learn when they went to the palace? _____

   _____

   _____

4. What was on every youth's mind when the seeds did not grow?

   _____

   _____

5. What must the youth have done to bring such beautiful flowers

   to the palace? _____

   _____

6. What made the queen so sad? _____

   _____

7. What qualities were required to follow in the queen's footsteps

   as the future ruler? _____

   _____

8. What brought a smile to the queen's face? _____

   _____

   _____

58

9. How did the queen show her joy at finding an honest young man?

_____

_____

VOCABULARY

Complete each of the sentences below using one of the following words:

germinate, appeared, tempted,
heir, courage, dozens, integrity,
prepares, standard, humiliating

1. Rafael was _____ to eat the chocolates but decided to wait until he could share them with his friends.

2. When Alfram realized that he was _____ his friend, he decided to stop teasing him.

3. It took _____ for Amanda to tell her friends that she did not like the way they talked about other people behind their backs.

4. As her father's _____, she would receive a handsome sum of money with which she intended to build a hospital.

5. If you leave the soybeans in water for a few days, they will _____ and you can eat the sprouts.

6. Kong showed his _____ by bringing the wallet he found immediately to the police.

7. She waited at the roadside for nearly an hour before the bus _____ in the distance.

8. _____ of people had heard the message on the radio and brought their children for vaccination.

9. Carlos tries to do his best in all that he does; he has a high _____ .

10. Before planting the seeds, the farmer _____ the soil by plowing the field.

DISCUSSION

Why is it necessary to have courage in order to always tell the truth?

MEMORIZATION

"Truthfulness is the foundation of all human virtues. Without truthfulness progress and success, in all the worlds of God, are impossible for any soul."

XVI

Too often we underestimate things because of their appearance. If we learn to look carefully, we see that even God's smallest creation has much to offer. Here is the story of how a lion came to understand this truth.

 Mouse was trembling. Almost everything frightened him. Almost everything was bigger than he was. Not only was Mouse small but he also felt small and insignificant.

Lion was not afraid of anything. He was strong and fierce. Convinced that nothing could harm him, he walked around full of confidence. And he seemed to be amused that little animals were frightened of him. That is why when he saw Mouse gathering seeds in the shadow of a small tree, he decided to strike. His big paw came down on Mouse and trapped him.

Mouse trembled. "O Great One, don't eat me," he said in fear.

"Why not?" asked Lion. "Surely, that is all you are good for!"

"But I am so small that I cannot be of any use to you as a meal," said Mouse. "Let me go and I will be your friend forever."

"A friend!" said Lion. "Of what use is your friendship to me?" he roared with laughter. "You make me laugh. It is good to laugh. For that I will let you go this time."

A few days later, while walking proudly through his territory, Lion noticed that several traps had been laid out by hunters. "Foolish hunters," he thought to himself. "They think they can catch me!" He walked carefully and avoided every one of the traps— every one, that is, but a net hanging in a tree. "Arrrr," roared Lion as the net crashed down on him. He struggled to free himself but, no matter how hard he tried, he could not.

Mouse, hearing all the noise, went over to find out what was happening. When he saw Lion caught in the net, he approached and said, "O Great One, I have come to help you."

"It is not a good laugh I need now," said Lion, "but strength and force!"

Mouse did not allow himself to be discouraged. He went to work. Thread by thread, he chewed through the ropes until there was a hole in the net and Lion was free!

Lion learned a good lesson that day, and he was noble enough to admit it. "I have misjudged you, my little friend," he said. "Your friendship turned out to be more valuable than all my power and strength."

COMPREHENSION

Answer the questions below in complete sentences.

1. How would you describe Mouse? _____

   _____

2. How would you describe Lion? _____

   _____

3. Why did Lion decide to attack Mouse? _____

   _____

   _____

4. With what did Lion trap Mouse? _____

   _____

5. What did Mouse ask Lion? _____

   _____

6. What did Lion answer? _____

_____

7. Why did Lion let Mouse go? _____

_____

8. What did Lion think of the hunters? _____

_____

9. Once trapped, what did Lion think was necessary to free

himself? _____

_____

10. What did Mouse do? _____

_____

11. What lesson did Lion learn that day? _____

_____

VOCABULARY

Complete each of the sentences below using one of the following words:

amused, underestimate, misjudged,
noble, avoid, discouraged, admitted,
insignificant, appearance, confidence

1. Ramses was _____ by the way the kittens played with each other.

2. After climbing for a while, Xi Zhao realized that he had _____ how long it would take to reach the top of the hill.

3. We should never _____ the power of friendship.

63

4. She had such a youthful _____ that it was hard to believe she was a university professor.

5. It is best to _____ planting the same crop in the same field year after year.

6. The amount of money it took to fix the old tractor was _____ compared with the cost of buying a new one.

7. Instead of being _____ by the difficulty of his homework, David decided to look up in the dictionary the words that he did not understand.

8. Alison was always truthful, courageous, and willing to help; her _____ character was admired by all of her friends.

9. He _____ to having many shortcomings, but said that dishonesty was not one of them.

10. She is shy, and it is difficult for her to speak in public, but she gains more and more _____ every time she tries.

DISCUSSION

How can we avoid being fooled by appearances?

MEMORIZATION

"One must see in every human being only that which is worthy of praise. When this is done, one can be a friend to the whole human race."

XVII

How often do we look at things only from our own point of view? How often do we consider only our own convenience? When we do this, we neglect both justice and compassion.

Grandfather had aged. His hands would shake, he had trouble seeing, and his hearing was not so good. Many of his teeth were missing, and he had constant aches and pains. In fact, he had become so feeble that he had difficulty feeding himself. During meals he would cough and wheeze, drop his food, and spill his soup.

Grandfather's condition gradually grew worse, and one evening during supper he dropped his soup bowl and broke it. Annoyed and upset, his son and daughter-in-law decided he could not eat at the table with them any longer. "What kind of an example do you think you are setting for your grandson?" they asked him. "How can we teach him decent table manners with such a bad example in front of him?" From then on, they told him, he would eat in his room alone.

A few days later, the father saw his young son carving something out of wood. Curious, he asked, "What are you making there?"

"I am carving a wooden bowl," was the innocent reply, "so that when you get old, you cannot break it and will not have to eat by yourself."

The father and mother looked at each other and felt ashamed. They realized that what their son needed was not a lesson in table manners, but the example of their loving kindness to his grandfather. And so the family learned to enjoy having meals together again.

COMPREHENSION

Answer the questions below in complete sentences.

1. What was Grandfather's condition? _____

_____

_____

2. What would happen to Grandfather while eating? _____

_____

_____

3. What happened that annoyed the son and daughter-in-law?

_____

_____

4. What were they concerned about? _____

_____

5. What was the grandson doing a few days later? _____

_____

6. Why did the father and mother feel ashamed? _____

_____

_____

7. What did they decide the grandson needed to see? _____

_____

_____

VOCABULARY

Complete each of the sentences on the next page using one of the following words:

> compassion, neglected, innocent,
> considered, ashamed, convenient,
> annoyed, carved, curious, manners

66

1. Using a sharp knife to cut small pieces from the wood, the artist _____ a beautiful eagle.

2. The parents were _____ about their daughter's first day at school and were eager to hear how it went.

3. His neighbors were _____ by his loud music.

4. Suzanne was full of _____ for the victims of the flood and did everything she could to help them.

5. He felt _____ to be doing nothing when everyone else around him was working so hard.

6. It was very _____ to live so close to the market.

7. Before reaching a decision, they listened to one another and _____ carefully every idea.

8. The child gave his mother an _____ look, but she knew he had been naughty.

9. The flower garden was _____ and full of weeds and dead plants.

10. Mothers should teach their children good _____ .

DISCUSSION

How does seeing things from other people's point of view help us to build friendships?

MEMORIZATION

> **"For the attributes of the people of faith are justice and fair-mindedness; forbearance and compassion and generosity; consideration for others; candor, trustworthiness, and loyalty; love and loving-kindness; devotion and determination and humanity."**

XVIII

To be free, we must learn to let go of some of the things we hold dear. This is a lesson a certain monkey had never learned.

Escaping from a band of village children who were determined to catch him, Monkey jumped from tree to tree in a panic. When he was sure that he had lost them, he calmed down, sat on a branch, and lazily looked around. Oh, how good it felt to be free!

His eyes caught sight of a squirrel busy gathering nuts. It would take a few nuts, enter the hollow of a tree through a hole, drop its load, come out, and run to gather more.

The oil of the nuts gave off a delicious scent that aroused Monkey's appetite. "Here is some easy food," he thought to himself and went closer to investigate. Unfortunately the hole was too small for him to enter, so he put his hand in. Down and down he reached and, to his delight, his hand finally touched the nuts. He hastily grabbed a few and tried to pull them out. But now his fist, closed around the nuts, was too big to come out through the hole.

He could not decide what to do. If he opened his hand, he would lose the nuts. But there was no way that his fist full of nuts would make it through the hole. So there he stood, unwilling to give up the nuts—not even when he heard the children's voices again. And as luck would have it, one of them spotted him. He saw the children running towards him, but still he would not let go of the nuts.

That is how he ended up sold to a zoo and spent the rest of his life in a cage.

COMPREHENSION

Answer the questions below in complete sentences.

1. What was Monkey running from? _____

_____

2. What was Monkey feeling during his escape? _____

_____

3. Once safe, what did Monkey see? _____

_____

4. What was the squirrel doing? _____

_____

_____

5. How did Monkey feel when he smelled the oil of the nuts?

_____

_____

6. How did Monkey feel when he closed his hand around the nuts?

_____

_____

7. What problem did Monkey face once he had the nuts? _____

_____

_____

8. What choices did Monkey have? _____

_____

_____

9. What did Monkey choose in the end? _____

_____

_____

10. What was the result of Monkey's choice? _____

_____

_____

VOCABULARY

Complete each of the sentences below using one of the following words:

panic, hastily, scent, gather,
unwilling, decided, aroused,
determined, investigate, band

1. Ines noticed the ants marching together and decided to _____ and find out what they were doing.

2. The boys _____ the anger of the bees when they accidentally moved the branch on which the hive was hanging.

3. Hearing the angry buzz, they ran away in a _____ .

4. The river was flooding quickly, so the family _____ gathered some clothes and went to a safe place.

5. Several days after the river had flooded, they _____ that it was safe to return to their home.

6. Roger was _____ to stay around when his friends began to play rough.

7. The police finally caught the _____ of thieves.

8. The warm breeze brought the _____ of the wild flowers to the bees.

9. Jose paid careful attention to the quality of the drinking water because he was _____ to keep his family healthy.

10. She went out to _____ wood for the fire.

71

DISCUSSION

What kinds of things do we need to let go of in order to grow spiritually?

MEMORIZATION

"No man shall attain the shores of the ocean of true understanding except he be detached from all that is in heaven and on earth."

XIX

It is easy to think that we are doing others a favor when we forgive them for the wrongs they have done. But we should remember that forgiveness is as much a comfort to our own souls as it is to the ones we forgive. A wise teacher once found a way to explain this to her students.

It brought the teacher great sadness to see that there was much rancor among her students. They would bicker and argue about the most insignificant things. They would constantly hurt one another's feelings. And then, rather than forgive and forget, they would carry around a grudge for days, sometimes weeks.

One morning the teacher gave each of the students an empty sack. In the front of the room was a basket full of potatoes. For every person who wronged them, she said, they should put a potato into their sacks. They should carry the sacks around with them for one month. "At the end of the month," she told them, "we shall compare sacks." The students thought this was a fine idea. But then she explained one more thing: If they forgave someone for what he or she had done, they should take out a potato and throw it away.

Slowly the sacks began to fill up, and by the end of the first week, a few of the students complained that they were becoming too heavy to carry. But this did not stop them from adding potatoes to their sacks, determined as they were to show how much they had been wronged by the others. By the time they reached the third week, some of the potatoes were decaying and giving off a nasty odor. Still the students were not deterred.

Finally one clever boy figured it out. He thought about his sack of potatoes. He thought about his classmates. Instead of all their wrongdoings, he remembered what good friends they had been to him. The more he thought about them, the more he realized how easily he could get rid of the potatoes. In one act of forgiveness, he threw the entire sack away. By the next day the teacher's point had been understood by all the students.

COMPREHENSION

Answer the questions below in complete sentences.

1. What saddened the teacher about her students? _____

   _____

   _____

2. How did the students behave towards one another? _____

   _____

   _____

   _____

3. What did the teacher bring to school one day? _____

   _____

   _____

4. What did she tell the students to do with the sacks and the

   potatoes? _____

   _____

   _____

5. What did the potatoes represent? _____

   _____

   _____

6. Why did the students continue to carry around the sacks when

   they became heavy and smelly? _____

   _____

   _____

7. What did one clever young boy finally figure out? _____

_____

_____

_____

VOCABULARY

Complete each of the sentences below using one of the following words:

> empty, rancor, complained,
> deter, decay, argue, constantly,
> explained, comparing, favor

1. After _____ prices, she decided to wait and buy the refrigerator when it was on sale.

2. He pointed to the _____ seat next to the man in the blue shirt and told me that I could sit there.

3. You should brush your teeth regularly, otherwise they will _____ .

4. Though she was in pain, she never _____ .

5. Nothing could _____ her from completing her daily tasks.

6. It _____ rains at this time of the year.

7. She does not like to _____ and prefers to remain silent.

8. The nurse _____ to the young mother how to care for her sick baby.

9. They argued often, but there was no _____ between them and they parted as friends.

10. He is a kind person who is willing to do a _____ for anyone.

75

DISCUSSION

How does forgiveness help the one that forgives?

MEMORIZATION

"But if he who has been struck pardons and forgives, he shows the greatest mercy. This is worthy of admiration."

XX

Communities advance through united action. Progress is made when all members take on their share of the work and contribute their talents. This is called the principle of universal participation. Someone explained this principle in the following way.

 Xvxn though my typxwritxr is an old modxl, it works quitx wxll xxcxpt for onx of thx kxys. I wish that it would work pxrfxctly. It is trux that thxrx arx forty-onx othxr kxys that function wxll xnough, but just onx kxy not working makxs all thx diffxrxncx.

It sxxms to mx that a community is not unlikx my typxwritxr. Anyonx of us could say, "Wxll, I am only onx pxrson. What I do won't makx or brxak thx community." That is trux. But xvxryonx doxs makx a diffxrxncx. A community nxxds thx activx participation of xvxry onx of its mxmbxrs. So nxxt timx you think your xfforts don't count, think of my typxwritxr and say to yoursxlf, "Although thxrx arx many pxoplx in thx community and things will gxt donx without mx, I must play my part. I won't bx a brokxn kxy."

COMPREHENSION

Answer the questions below in complete sentences.

1. What is the matter with the typewriter in this reading? _____

_____

2. What letter does 'x' take the place of in the reading? _____

_____

3. How many keys of the typewriter function? _____

_____

77

4. What is the effect of the one key that does not function? ____

_____

_____

5. What does a community need from its members? _____

_____

_____

VOCABULARY

Complete each of the sentences below using one of the following words:

> participation, unlike, functioned,
> principles, contributed, advance,
> universal, model, progress, share

1. Although there was less food than expected, the youth were content with their _____ and did not ask for more.

2. The principle of justice is _____ , for it is accepted by all people.

3. The old man was allowed to _____ to the front of the line.

4. _____ does not come without effort.

5. Kenji was excited about the insect he found because it was _____ any he had seen before.

6. Everyone _____ time and money to the project.

7. When everyone contributes something to a project, we say there has been universal _____ .

8. He was curious to see how the clock _____ so decided to take it apart.

9. He is just, compassionate, and honest; he is a person who lives by his _____ .

10. When she went to buy a new bicycle, Rachael had difficulty deciding which _____ to choose.

DISCUSSION

Think of your community as a human body. What happens when one organ of the body does not work properly?

MEMORIZATION

"So powerful is the light of unity that it can illuminate the whole earth."